Ma… …s
and …
Beach B…

Jane West

Illustrated by
Stik

RISING STARS

Rising Stars UK Ltd.
7 Hatchers Mews, Bermondsey Street, London SE1 3GS
www.risingstars-uk.com

Published 2008
Reprinted 2009, 2010, 2011

Cover design: Burville-Riley Partnership
Illustrator: Stik, Bill Greenhead for Illustration
Text design and typesetting: Andy Wilson
Publisher: Gill Budgell
Editor: Jane Wood

British Library Cataloguing in Publication Data.
A CIP record for this book is available from the British Library

ISBN: 978 1 84680 337 6

Printed in the UK by Ashford Colour Press Ltd.

Contents

Meet the Magic Mates

The Magic Mates are best friends – but that doesn't mean they're all alike.

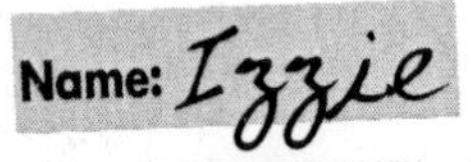

The sporty one: can climb trees, surf and take on the boys at their own game – and win.

Travels by: running!

Loves: trendy tracksuits, open skies and sandy beaches.

Hates: standing still.

Name: Meena

The girly one: uses her mobile for networking and planning her social life.

Travels by: Mum's car (her personal chauffeur).

Loves: pink and her Magic Mates.

Hates: breaking a nail.

Name: Ginger

The ginger one: you don't wanna mess with this feisty gal – the Kung Fu and quick quip queen!

Travels by: push-scooter.

Loves: Jackie Chan and her Magic Mate pals.

Hates: nail extensions.

Name: Jo

The clever one: uses her brains and quick wit to talk her way out of trouble. Sometimes she's a bit too quick.

Travels by: bicycle and is designing a pair of motorised rollerblades.

Loves: Jacqueline Wilson, Cathy Cassidy and Albert Einstein.

Hates: being called 'geek', 'nerd', 'swot' or 'boffin'.

Name: Ellie

The fashion-conscious one: can tell her Prada from her Asda and knows how to accessorise.

Travels by: limousine, of course! (But only in her dreams.)

Loves: shopping.

Hates: anything to do with getting dirty; anyone who upsets her Magic Mates.

Name: Yash

The funky punky one: the 'alternative' one of the gang who hugs trees, people and furry animals.

Travels by: skateboard.

Loves: having a good time.

Hates: bullies.

1

Beach Break

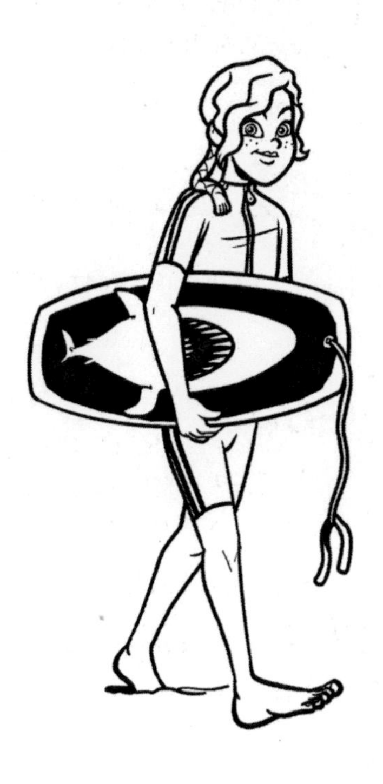

The Magic Mates are enjoying their day at the beach. The sun is warm, the ice creams are cold and the waves are big. It's perfect for Izzie. She's hoping to win the bodyboarding surf competition.

Izzie	Look at those waves! They're nearly a metre high. Perfect!
Ginger	Great! I love jumping through the waves.
Meena	Perfect for you two. I'm not going swimming in those waves – I'd get my hair wet.

Jo Well, you can stay on the beach. Don't forget to wear lots of sun cream and your hat.

Yash Look, Meena. You can go to that swimming pool over there. You can have a swim and still not get your hair wet.

Ellie I think I'll come, too. Don't worry, Izzie. We'll be back in time to see you win the bodyboarding competition.

Izzie	Hmm. Maybe. There are some really good bodyboarders here. But it would be great to win. The first prize is a holiday on a cruise ship for six people. Guess who I'd take?
Yash	Your Magic Mates?!
Izzie	Ha ha! Good guess.
Meena	I really hope you win. A cruise would be brilliant. I'll cross my fingers for you.
Jo	We're all supporting you, Izzie.
Izzie	I just want to do my best.

Ellie and Meena go to the swimming pool.
Yash decides to go for a walk
along the beach. Jo is reading her book.
It's all about sharks, but she decides
not to tell Ginger and Izzie,
who are going bodyboarding.
(Luckily, Jo will read that there aren't
any dangerous sharks in British waters –
phew!)

Ginger Bodyboarding is a lot harder than it looks.
You make it look so easy!

Izzie Don't worry, Ginger.
You'll soon get the hang of it.

Ginger decides to have another go. This time she rides the wave all the way into the beach.

Ginger Yeeeeeeah! Wow!
That was brilliant!
It felt so fast!

Izzie Yes, it's the best feeling
in the world when you catch
a wave and ride it.
Well done, Ginger!
Now you're surfing!

2

Double Trouble

Izzie and Ginger have just got time to have an ice cream before the competition starts. They walk towards the ice cream van.

Ginger I can't decide whether to have a Soft 'n' Swirly or a Cookie Crumble.

Izzie Yum! I'd like a Peanut Cluster or a Chocolate Surprise.

Ginger Maybe I'll have both!
I'm really hungry after all
that bodyboarding.

Izzie Yes. Top sportspeople always eat
bananas to give them energy.
I think I'll have a banana-
flavoured ice cream with
a chocolate flake.

Ginger I've never seen a top sportsperson
eat one of those!

Izzie Maybe I'll be the first!
Ha ha!

The girls are still deciding what to have when Izzie sees two small children. They are the toddlers who live next door to her! But Toby and Tom seem to be alone. Where are their parents?

Izzie Hey, kids! Where's your mum?

Ginger You toddlers shouldn't be here by yourself.

Toby Boo!

Tom Boo, boo!

Izzie Oh dear. I think they're lost.

Ginger I bet their parents are worried. They must be on the beach somewhere.

Izzie We should take them to the lifeguards. They will help them to find their parents.

Ginger That's a good idea.

Izzie Come on, you two.
We're going to get some help
to find your mummy and daddy.

Toby No!

Tom No, no!

Ginger Oh dear. What do we do now?

S.O.S.

Izzie and Ginger don't know what to do next. The two naughty toddlers won't go with them. Izzie knows that if you get lost on the beach, you should always go to the lifeguard. These toddlers are very naughty!

Izzie You keep an eye on them and I'll go and find the lifeguard. He'll know what to do.

Ginger That's a good idea.

It is a good idea, but the toddlers don't know that. One of them is toddling towards the sea and those big waves. The other is toddling after a red beach ball.

Ginger Well, it *was* a good idea …

Izzie I'll get the one who is heading for the sea.

Ginger I'll get the one who is chasing the beach ball.

The toddlers aren't pleased.
In fact, they're very cross.
They start screaming. Soon the toddlers are red in the face. A kind-looking lady comes over to help them.

Lady You look like you're having some trouble with those two. Are they your little brothers?

Ginger No, thank goodness!

Izzie They live next door to me.
We found them on their own.
We were worried they'd
get into trouble.

Ginger We wanted to take them
to the lifeguard but they
wouldn't go.

Lady Don't worry, girls. I'll go
and tell the lifeguard.
He'll find their parents.
I'll be as quick as I can.

Just then the girls hear a voice
on the loudspeaker. The bodyboarding
contest is starting. Now what will Izzie do?

Ginger You have to go!

Izzie I can't leave you with this lot
of double trouble on your own.

Ginger I'll be fine.

Izzie No, you'll need all the help you can get with these two!

Ginger What about the competition?

Izzie Maybe next year.

Ginger knows that Izzie is upset about missing the competition, but these two toddlers are really a handful. If only she could help her.

Rescued!

The bodyboarders are getting ready for the competition. Izzie can only watch sadly as she hangs on to a screaming toddler. Now both toddlers are trying to jump in the sea. Those waves are too big for babies.

Both girls hope that the kind-looking lady will come back with the lifeguard soon.

Ginger Let's help them build a sandcastle.

Izzie That's a good idea. Hey, kids! Want to make a sandcastle?

Toby Ya!

Tom Ya, ya!

Ginger I think that means 'yes'!

Izzie We could make a sand drawing instead of a sandcastle. Let's make it the shape of a big wave.

Ginger Yes! And I've got another idea.

The girls and the toddlers start making a huge sand drawing. Can you guess what it's going to be a picture of?

Just as the girls are finishing their sand drawing, the kind lady comes back with the lifeguard. He's got two worried-looking people with him.

Izzie Thank goodness for that! Here are their mum and dad.

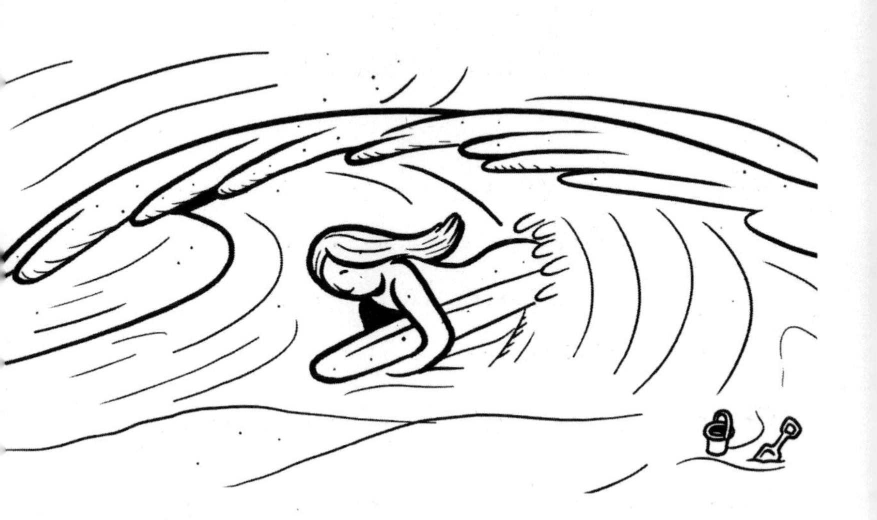

Lifeguard Hello, girls. I hear you've been having some trouble.

Ginger Yes, double trouble!
These two toddlers lost
their mum and dad.

Worried mum
Oh, you naughty boys!
Where have you been?
We've been so worried!

Toby Goo!

Tom Ga ga!

Worried dad

You're very lucky that Izzie and her friend found you.

Worried mum

Thank you so much!

Worried dad

Yes, thank you, girls.

Izzie I'm just glad they're back with you!

The happy parents walk back along the beach. The happy toddlers wave goodbye to Izzie and Ginger.

Lifeguard That's a really good sand drawing you've done. It looks just like a bodyboarder riding a wave.

Ginger Izzie is a really good bodyboarder.

Lifeguard How come you're not in the competition?

Izzie Oh, well …

Ginger She should have been,
but we were looking after
the toddlers.

Lifeguard I'll fix that. Come on, girls!

The lifeguard zooms off down the beach.
He talks to the people organising
the competition and points at Izzie.

Lifeguard I've told them all about you. They were so impressed that they're going to give you a chance.

Izzie Wow! Thank you so much!

Ginger Go on, Izzie! Show them what you can do!

Izzie jumps into the sea with her bodyboard. Soon she's riding a wave and everyone on the beach is cheering.

Ginger is jumping up and down.

Ginger Go, Izzie! Go, Izzie!

Lifeguard Your friend really is good!

Ginger She's my mate! She's magic!

Izzie rides a wave all the way into the beach. Ginger runs up and gives her a big hug.

Ginger You were brilliant!

Izzie I was just glad to be able to have a go.

The judges have made their choices.

Judge In third place is Sandi Bottom.

Crowd Hurrah!

Judge In second place is Sunny Summers.

Crowd Hurrah!

Judge In first place is Izzie!

Crowd Hurrah!

Ginger Yeeah! Hooray! Hooray!

Izzie I don't believe it!

Ginger Cruise ship here we come!

Izzie goes up to the judges to collect her prize. They give her a silver cup.

Judge You are a very good bodyboarder. But it's very good to know that you also care about beach safety. Well done, Izzie!

Izzie	Thank you very much!
Ginger	Maybe I could enter the bodyboarding competition next year. What do you think?
Izzie	I think you should stick to the sand sculpture instead! Come on, we've got a holiday to start planning for!

About the Author

Jane West loves bodyboarding. It's one of her favourite things to do. She's not as good as Izzie, but she has lots of fun trying!

Jane West:

- lives by the beach in Cornwall
- likes taking her dog Pip paddling in the sea
- has worked in an art gallery, a bookshop and a school.

Now she's a writer, and has had great fun writing about the Magic Mates. She hopes you liked reading about them.

The History of Surfing

Surfing started thousands of years ago on some islands in the Pacific Ocean. The islanders made logs into canoes to paddle between the islands. Eventually they stood up on them to ride in the waves for fun.

Captain Cook first saw surfing when he stopped off in Hawaii on his voyage to discover Australia in 1778. One of his officers wrote:

'Whenever the surf is increased to its utmost heights, they choose that time for this amusement: twenty or thirty of the natives, taking each a long narrow board, rounded at the ends, set out together from the shore ... The boldness with which we saw them perform was altogether astonishing.'

Men, women, boys and girls all surfed together.

Strange But True – Surf Facts

- A Cornish ice cream seller, Pip Staffieri, built his own surfboard and taught himself to surf. His board was so heavy, he had to wheel it to the beach on a baby's pram!
- Over 300,000 people surf in the UK. Over 75,000 are women and girls.
- The tide on the beach is caused by the moon!
- A wave hitting a beach in Cornwall, Devon or South Wales could have travelled over 4000 miles across the Atlantic.
- The first person in the UK to ride a surfboard standing up was a dentist on holiday in Cornwall, in 1937. His name was Jimmy Dix.

Surf Lingo

Air or catching air When a surfer or bodyboarder jumps out of the top of a wave.

Aloha Traditional Hawaiian greeting

Beach break A wave that breaks over the sandy sea bed.

Dude What American surfers call other surfers.

Fins What bodyboarders wear on their feet to help them paddle through the sea.

Grommet A young surfer.

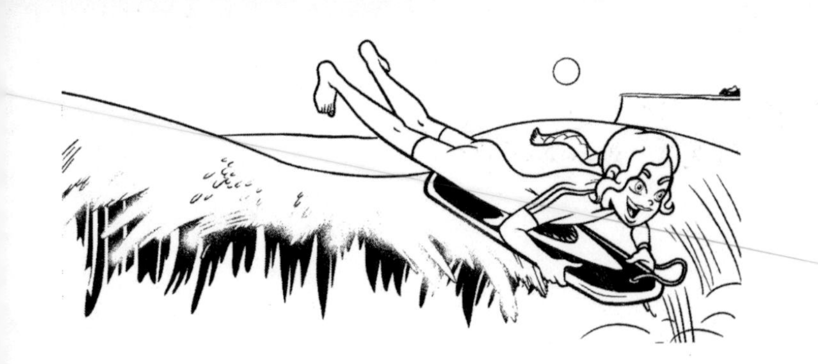

Offshore wind Wind blowing from the sea onto the land. Ideal surfing conditions.

Onshore wind Wind blowing from the land onto the sea. Spoils waves for surfing.

S.O.S. Help! It's the message that ships send to the coastguard if they're in trouble.
It stands for 'Save Our Souls'.

Stoked Very happy, as in: 'Wow!
What a great ride! I'm totally stoked!'

Wetsuit A suit that keeps you warm in the water. Made of a material called neoprene. A shortie wetsuit has no arms or legs.

Wipeout Fall off, as in: '[Cough, splutter]
I really got wiped out that time!'

Beach Safety

Do you know about beach safety?

Red and yellow flags – this area is watched by lifeguards and is the safest place to swim.

Black and white chequered flags – this area is for surfers, and canoes and kayaks. Don't swim here.

Red flag – danger! Don't go in.

Orange windsock – wind conditions are dangerous – don't take a blow-up boat into the sea.

Always swim or surf with a friend, never alone.

Listen to what the lifeguard tells you.

Slip, slap, slop! Be safe in the sun: slip on a T-shirt, slap on a hat, slop on some sun cream.

To find out more about being safe on the beach, go to www.beachsafety.org.uk.

Surf Jokes

Why didn't
the skeleton catch
the wave?

Because he didn't
have any guts!

Why is the sea
a friendly place?

Because
if you get lonely you can
wave and the sea will
wave back!

Surfing Quiz

1. If you are bodyboarding, should you swim between the black and white flags?
2. Do girls go surfing and bodyboarding?
3. What should you do if you see a red flag flying on the beach?
4. Translate this into surf speak: "I'm very happy about jumping my bodyboard out of the water, my surfing friend."
5. Where was Captain Cook going when he stopped off in Hawaii?

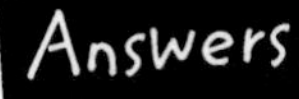

1 No. That's for surfers, kayakers and canoeists. Bodyboarders should go in the area that's safe for swimming, between the red and yellow flags.

2 Yes! Over 75,000 in the UK.

3 Don't go in the water. The red flag means 'danger'.

4 'I'm totally stoked about catching air, dude!'

5 He was on his way to discover Australia.

How did you score?

0–1 What a wipeout! You'd better send an S.O.S!

2–3 Not bad, but did the onshore wind get to you?

4–5 Fantastic! You must be totally stoked with that score!

Magic Mates

RISING STARS

Magic Mates books are available from most booksellers.

For mail order information
please call Rising Stars on 0800 091 1602
or visit www.risingstars-uk.com